Phonics Reading
Book 3 • Short i

The Magic School Bus®
Sticks to It

by Quinlan B. Lee

SCHOLASTIC INC.

New York   Toronto   London   Auckland   Sydney
Mexico City   New Delhi   Hong Kong   Buenos Aires

"Today is spider day, kids," says Ms. Frizzle. "Let us take a spin!" "Ick!" says Arnold.

The bus spins
and spins.
It spins into a bug.
"I feel sick," says Tim.

"Do you see that big spider?" asks Wanda.
"It has eight eyes," says Tim.
"I think it sees us!"

Spiders spin
sticky webs.
Bugs stick to the webs.
"Then what?" Tim asks.

Then the spider
eats the bugs!
"Ick!" says Ralphie.
"Now I feel sick," says
Wanda.

Look at that
big spider!
It sees us.
It thinks we
are a big bug!

The spider
did not eat us.
"I don't think it can!"
says Ms. Frizzle.

"This web is sticky!"
says Ralphie.
"We will cut the bus out of
the web," says Ms. Frizzle.